Writer Jin-hee Gang

She studied literary arts in college and worked as a TV screenwriter. She now creates fun content for children. Her major works include *Who? Special: Son Heung-min.*

Illustrator Hye-jin Lee

She is a professional illustrator who tells the story of the world in bright and beautiful pictures. She draws fun and exciting Learning Cartoons for children and, by extension, is working on a variety of projects as a channel for communication that is beneficial to people.

 K-pop

BTS

First Published June 2020

Writer Jin-hee Gang | **Illustrator** Hye-jin Lee
Translator Ji-hee Rhee, Kelsey Ulrich-Verslycken | **Supervisor** Heidi Nam

Publisher Sun-sik Kim
Publishing Company Studio Dasan

Management Director Eun-young Kim
Contents Development Director Jeong-eun Chae
Contents Development Team 1 Hee-jung Sim, Se-mi Park, Hee-seon Jeon, Yu-sun Kwon, Jeong-im Nam, Seo-won Choi
Marketing Director Gun-hong Do
Marketing Team 1 Ha-na Oh, Yeong-eun Yu **Marketing Team 2** Ji-hye Ahn, So-yeong Lee
Marketing Team 3 Ho-sung An
Sales Director Sun-hee Oh
Sales Team Sun-hee Lee, Ji-young Jo, Min-jae Kang
Business Management Division Dae-woo Hur, Mi-sun Ha, Sang-min Park, Hyeong-jun Kim, Min-a Kim, So-hee Lee, Wan-gyu Choi, Woo-chul Lee

© 2020 Studio Dasan

Printed and bound in Republic of Korea

STUDIO DASAN
Address 357, Hoedong-gil, Paju-si, Gyeonggi-do, Republic of Korea (2nd Floor)
Phone +82-2-703-1723 **Fax** +82-70-8233-1727
Online Community cafe.naver.com/dasankids
"who?" Series Online Mall www.whomall.co.kr

ISBN 979-11-5639-467-9(14990)

· The price of the book is on the back cover.
· Photos in this book are sourced from Shutterstock, Wikipedia, Yonhap News, etc.

BTS

Studio Dasan

The world's most beloved stars, BTS!

Who? K-pop BTS is about
how seven boys who dreamed of becoming singers
grew into a global sensation named BTS: their story,
their success, and their fans who love
and support them.

CONTENTS

RM

♥ **Name:** Nam-joon Kim
♥ **Date of birth:** September 12th, 1994
♥ **Hometown:** Ilsan, South Korea
♥ **Height:** 181 cm
♥ **Blood type:** A
♥ **Favorites:** Figurines / Clothes

Me and all of my people will end up winning in the end very naturally, while no one is looking.

JIN

- ♥ **Name:** Seok-jin Kim
- ♥ **Date of birth:** December 4th, 1992
- ♥ **Hometown:** Gwacheon, South Korea
- ♥ **Height:** 178 cm
- ♥ **Blood type:** O
- ♥ **Favorites:** Dad jokes / Fishing / SUPER MARIO

I know your troubles, so you only need to know your hard work.

SUGA

♥ **Name:** Yoon-gi Min

♥ **Date of birth:** March 9th, 1993

♥ **Hometown:** Daegu, South Korea

♥ **Height:** 174 cm

♥ **Blood type:** O

♥ **Favorites:** Relaxing lying down

I thought I'd always be happy above the clouds, but sometimes I'm afraid to look down. We are encouraged to fly together. I'm afraid of falling, but I'm not afraid of landing.

J-HOPE

- ♥ **Name:** Ho-seok Jung
- ♥ **Date of birth:** February 18th, 1994
- ♥ **Hometown:** Gwangju, South Korea
- ♥ **Height:** 178 cm
- ♥ **Blood type:** A
- ♥ **Favorites:** Interior Design / Figurines / Acorn bag

I'm your hope. You're my hope.
I'm J-Hope.

JIMIN

- ♥ **Name:** Ji-min Park
- ♥ **Date of birth:** October 13th, 1995
- ♥ **Hometown:** Busan, South Korea
- ♥ **Height:** 173 cm
- ♥ **Blood type:** A
- ♥ **Favorites:** Eating Pork cutlets and Kimchi-jjigae

I hope your happy smile is
not just a smile.
That's all I want for you.

♥ **Name:** Tae-hyung Kim

♥ **Date of birth:** December 30th, 1995

♥ **Hometown:** Daegu & Geochang, South Korea

♥ **Height:** 178 cm

♥ **Blood type:** AB

♥ **Favorites:** Eating Hamburgers and Jajangmyeon /
Photography

I love you more than yesterday,
less than tomorrow.

JUNG KOOK

- ♥ **Name:** Jung-kook Jeon
- ♥ **Date of birth:** September 1st, 1997
- ♥ **Hometown:** Busan, South Korea
- ♥ **Height:** 178 cm
- ♥ **Blood type:** A
- ♥ **Favorites:** Exercising / Videography / Gaming

I would be really happy if I could do anything to help you with your life.

ARMY
WILL ALWAYS
BE TOGETHER WITH BTS

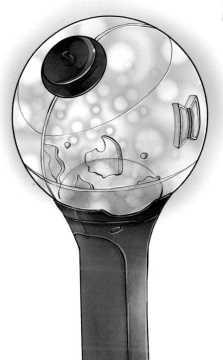

♥ **Name:** A.R.M.Y.

♥ **Meaning:**

1) BTS and their fans are always together, just like soldiers and their bulletproof body armor.

2) **A**dorable **R**epresentative **M**.C. for Youth

♥ **Inauguration:** March 29th, 2014

PROLOGUE

• UN (United Nations)
An international organization established to prevent wars and maintain peace

September 24th, 2018, UN• Headquarters in New York, the United States

"Generation Unlimited•," a project by the UN and UNICEF•, was announced during the 73rd General Assembly of the United Nations. BTS attended the meeting to represent youth around the world.

And now, let's hear from BTS.

• UNICEF (United Nations Children's Fund) A special UN organization established to provide relief to children affected by wars and to improve welfare for children in underdeveloped countries
• Generation Unlimited A global partnership program started to expand investments and opportunities for children and young adults 10 to 24 years old

RM, the leader of BTS, begins to speak*.

• **The Full UN Speech by RM** ••• pp. 156~157

This is the story of BTS, the first Korean pop music group to give a speech at the UN General Assembly. Their mission was to deliver a message of hope to youth around the world.

CHAPTER ✦ 1

SEVEN BOYS, ONE DREAM 1

That evening

Are you serious? I won't allow it.

Come on, Dad! Please!

Do you really want to pursue this? It won't be easy.

I'm not doing this just because it's cool. I want to share my thoughts through rap music.

All right. But no matter how rough it gets, you can't give up.

Thanks Dad! I won't let you down!

Although his parents initially were against it, they finally agreed that he should follow his dream of becoming a rapper.

In his middle school days, Nam-joon gained popularity as an amateur rapper going by the name Runch Randa.

Yo! Look at me! Who dat? It's Randa! Runch Randa!

Hey! Who's that kid?

Sleepy (Rapper)

That's Runch Randa. Can you believe he's still in middle school? Just imagine what he could become in a few years!

A middle school kid? How can a kid come up with such complex and powerful verses?

Sleepy, a rapper in the group Untouchable, was amazed by Nam-joon's performance.

Gangnam, Seoul, Big Hit Entertainment office

Si-hyuk Bang (Producer / CEO of Big Hit Entertainment)

WHAT?

Hey boss, I think you should take a look at this kid.

Sleepy saw him at a concert. He says this kid's got talent.

BIG HIT
Entertainment

Pdogg
(Music Producer)

Wow! Look at how he's playing with the beat. No one would think the verses were by a middle school kid. They have such depth and meaning!

Get in touch with him, ASAP!

What?
He totally revamped
the audition beat.

Amazing skills!

I'm going to
ace the preliminary
audition.

ACCEPTED

Yoon-gi passed the preliminary round with flying colors and went on to the final audition.

Three boys from three different places but with the same dream came together as trainees for Big Hit Entertainment.

CHAPTER ★ 2

SEVEN BOYS,
ONE DREAM 2

Seok-jin, who wanted to be an actor, entered Konkuk University to study theater and film.

Theater and Film Department Concert

He's so handsome!

I heard he was approached by a casting agent on the streets yesterday. He will be on TV in no time.

Seok-jin, I heard you got approached again. Are you going to be a celebrity soon?

WOW!

In 2011, the national audition for *Super Star K 3*, a TV audition program on the cable channel Mnet, was held.

Are all these people auditioning today? There's so much competition!

Will I be able to come out on top?

Jung-kook Jeon
(Jungkook)

These are all famous entertainment companies. Even though I didn't pass the audition, they gave me these and said I have potential.

Really? They saw my boy's hidden talents!

What should I do?

Let's find a place that will help realize your potential to the fullest.

After moving to Seoul, Jung-kook tried to decide which company would be the best fit for him.

Jung-kook was inspired when he saw Nam-joon practice, and decided to be a Big Hit Entertainment trainee.

Wow!

He's awesome! I wish I could be on his team!

Tae-hyung applied to an art high school to become a saxophone player, but instead, settled on a regular high school after receiving a rejection letter.

SIGH...

Hey, dancing is fun.

He began taking dance classes with his friends.

Then one day

Today is the day!

Big Hit Global Audition

Big Hit Entertainment? It's not a very big company….

But we could be training to be professionals.

Yeah, but there are so many people wanting to be singers these days.

Too bad you're not going. You're a good dancer. See you when we get back.

Good luck! I'll be rooting for you guys!

If they make it, they'll be trained to become professional singers!

Aren't you auditioning?

Big Hit Global Audition

At the suggestion of one of the judges, Tae-hyung decided to audition.

Busan, 2011

I really love dancing. I want to dance like Rain*.

Ji-min Park (Jimin)

Hey, Ji-min!

I hear you got accepted at Busan High School of Arts with the highest score? Congrats!

Yeah, thanks.

Ji-min, who loved to dance, took modern dance classes and entered Busan High School of Arts.

• **Rain** A famous Korean singer and actor

Busan High School of Arts

Let's try this. Use your arms and back….

This move is too hard. Can you show it to me again?

Not now, I'm going to practice a little more before heading out.

Ji-min, aren't you going home? We're leaving now!

Nam-joon

Yoon-gi

Ho-seok

Seok-jin

We finally got all of them! Now, let's begin!

Jung-kook

Tae-hyung

Ji-min

The seven boys have finally come together. What kind of future awaits them?

CHAPTER ★ 3

A TRAINEE'S ORDINARY DAY

What should we call them once they debut? Should I use the name BTS?

Young Nation···?

Big Kids···?

When I was talking with the trainees, I found out that they wanted to connect to kids their age. They wanted to tell their own stories in their own voices.

I am sure the audience will relate to us if we tell them our stories.

I'm thinking of writing songs about teens and young adults.

• **Jung team-jang (Jung team leader)** Ho-seok was called Jung team-jang, the dance team leader

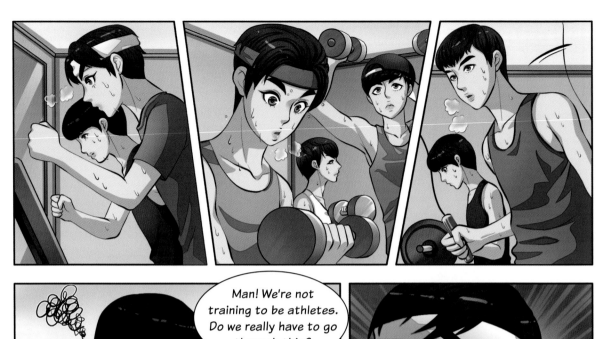

• **Bangtan Room** The studio where BTS members work

Mr. Bang….

Emergency Room

Am I going to get kicked off of the team because of my shoulder injury?

I had to earn money for school and living expenses.

You should have told me about it. We will help out with your tuition so you can just focus on getting better.

Thank you.

Yoon-gi focused on his rehab treatment.

I can't give up like this. I'm going to debut!

How's practice going?

It's awesome. A lot of great singers joined in.

But when are you debuting? You've been training since 2010.

I know. I'm afraid everything is just going to disappear one day.

But I'm keeping my hopes up.

I'm going back to practice. See you later, bro.

So soon?

• On November 13th, 2017, Rap Monster changed his stage name to RM to better suit the style he was aiming for.

Big Hit Entertainment was not as large as other big entertainment companies at the time. Mr. Bang was trying hard to stay afloat in a sea of competition.

These kids were all hand-picked and raised by me. We need something special if we are going to take on those larger entertainment companies.

Hey, kids!

Now that all the members of BTS have been decided on,

let's show the world who you are through videos before your debut.

BTS created an SNS• account to upload their music and used social media channels to communicate with people.

八道江山 팔도강산

BTS "Rap Monster" by Rap Monster

• **SNS** Social Network Services

All the members practiced tirelessly for their debut day, and the videos of them practicing and talking about their lives that they posted on social media gave them a solid fan base, even before their debut.

CHAPTER ★ 4

BLOOD, SWEAT,
AND TEARS

Hey, guys!

Check out this documentary. Seems like a story we can all relate to.

School of Tears

The three-part documentary *School of Tears* aired for three weeks from January 13th, 2013, to analyze the source of school bullying in Korea and eradicate bullying in school.

School Withdraw Form

After watching the documentary, the members started making music specifically for teenagers.

School is a war zone. There are victims and perpetrators, and everyone else seems to just be watching from the sidelines.

In January 2013, they released a pre-debut mixtape* titled "School of Tears."

• **Mixtape** Songs or albums released for free online, instead of on a CD or paid website. These are mostly released by R&B or hip-hop artists.

Congratulations Graduates!

Graduation certificate

Our baby boy is finally leaving middle school! You're all grown-up!

Thanks, guys.

Jung-kook! Congratulations!

The strenuous training continued after Jungkook returned from the US. The members added workouts to their practice regimen to build endurance.

Even during their practice sessions, the members continued to produce music, to film themselves practicing and talking about their lives, and to post the videos on their social media channels.

Wow! Is this really our Twitter page?

FOLLOWERS
1,200

We got more than a thousand followers in just a month! We've got 1,200 already!

Let's do this!

Before their official debut concert, BTS focused on recording their debut album.

Hold on! This part should be sung with a little more emotion and emphasis.

I'm sorry... my throat doesn't feel quite right.

COUGH

COUGH

I know it's hard, but there's no other way! The public can be ruthless.

If you want to be confident in front of a crowd, you have to be perfect!

Yes, sir!

Man, that was hard!

Do you think people will notice how much hard work we put into this? What if they don't like us?

Yeah, now that our debut is creeping up, I'm worried that no one will care about us.

I heard that many groups disappear as soon as they make their debut···.

Don't even say that! We've been doing our best for the past three years. Our efforts will be recognized, and people will love us!

No wonder you're the leader! I feel so much better after hearing that. Let's go through that song one more time! Everybody up!

The members were always tired because the training sessions got even harder before the debut. But they encouraged each other to achieve their dream and focused on practicing, just thinking about the fans who were waiting for them.

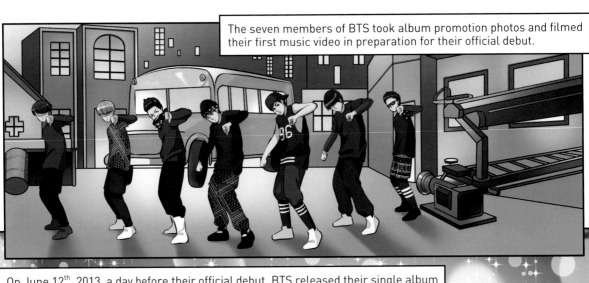

The seven members of BTS took album promotion photos and filmed their first music video in preparation for their official debut.

On June 12th, 2013, a day before their official debut, BTS released their single album *2 COOL 4 SKOOL*, and showcased it at the Ilji Art Hall in Cheongdam, Seoul.

June 13th

BTS

On June 13th, 2013, BTS took the first big step of a long journey to fulfill their dream.

CHAPTER ★ 5

SPOKESPEOPLE FOR TEENS

BTS successfully finished their debut performance.

Hey kids!

BTS

BAM!

Great job out there today! You must've been nervous, but you all looked so natural on the stage.

Do you think people are going to like us?

Not everyone is going to like you. Try not to feel hurt by what some people say.

Let's go get ready for the next show.

BTS

B

We've got a brand-new hip-hop group with us today who have brought with them some bold new music.

BTS!

BTS got to star in their own reality TV show starting in September of 2013 called *Rookie King Channel BTS*.

We came here a lot during our training. During our school vacation, we would eat two meals a day here!

In this program, BTS would reenact different games from other variety shows. *Rookie King Channel BTS* was a great way for the group to promote themselves to a wider audience.

On September 11th, 2013, BTS's first mini-album *O!RUL8,2?* was released. The album ranked 4th overall in the Gaon Album Chart•.

September 11th, 2013

Album Title	Artist	Producer
1. ------	------	------
2. ------	------	------
3. ------	------	------
4. O!RUL8,2?	BTS	BIG HIT

• **Gaon Album Chart** A Korean music chart that tallies and updates total album sales of artists every week

Everybody say "No!"

On November 14th, 2013, the 2013 Melon Music Awards were held at the Olympic Gymnastics Arena in Seoul.

CLICK!

CLICK!

I can't believe we're at an awards ceremony. It's like we're in a dream.

We promised each other that we'd get here. Now we're nominees for the Rookie Award!

Despite their popularity and busy schedule, BTS practiced even harder to keep improving for their fans.

And BTS still found the time to communicate with their fans on social media.

They worked tirelessly on improving their singing and dancing so that every performance was better than the last.

CHAPTER ☆ 6

KEEP PUSHING YOUR LIMITS!

On February 12th, 2014, a mini-album *Skool Luv Affair*, the final part of the "School Trilogy," was released.

Olympic Hall, Seoul Olympic Park, March 29th, 2014

Ten months after their debut, BTS's fan club was founded at an event entitled '2014 BTS: 1st Fan Meeting MUSTER.'

The official fan club's name was A.R.M.Y., which was selected by the BTS members from fan submissions.

BTS later began performing in Japan as well. Their Japanese debut single, *No More Dream (Japanese Ver.)*, was released on June 4th, 2014, and was placed 8th in the Oricon• Single Weekly Chart. Their second single, *Boy In Luv (Japanese Ver.)*, was released on July 16th, and ranked 4th in the same chart.

〈No More Dream (Japa
防彈少年團

發賣日　2014年　6月 4日

play　replay　stop

8
★

〈Boy In Luv(Japanese Ver.)〉
防彈少年團

發賣日　2014年　7月 16日

play　replay　stop

4
★

• **Oricon Chart** A Japanese music chart that went official in 1968 and is one of the top-three global music charts along with the Billboard Chart from the U.S. and the U.K. Chart from Britain

On August 20th, 2014, BTS released their first regular album *Dark & Wild.*

DARK&WILD

WARNING!
LOVEHURTS.IT CAUSES ANGER, JEALOUSY,
OBSESSION. WHY DON'T U LOVE ME BACK?

Melon-AX Hall●, Seoul, October 17th, 2014

THE RED BULLET

I've never felt so nervous in my life!

Don't worry, we've got the ARMY on our side. We can do this!

Let's show our fans how much we appreciate them by giving our best performance yet!

● **Melon-AX Hall** A performance venue, currently called YES24 Live Hall

The first BTS concert 'BTS LIVE TRILOGY EPISODE II: THE RED BULLET,' held over 3 days, was very successful. After the Seoul concert, BTS went on an Asian tour to solidify their overseas fan base.

Up until now, all of our albums have been about teenage school life, right?

So what do you think about us starting to talk about love and the interests of people more our age?

That's a good idea. It'll help our fans relate to us even more.

I agree. I want our fans to find comfort and encouragement in our music.

YEAH!

BTS

We should start to put more of our own ideas into the songs, then....

How about we all participate in the production?

Good idea! That could really help our album feel more personal and authentic.

What are my own ideas and feelings...?

All of the members collaborated to write lyrics and compose music for their new album.

What if we put that new melody here in this part of the song?

That's great!

On April 29th, 2015, BTS released a mini-album entitled *The Most Beautiful Moment in Life, Pt. 1*. The title song, "I Need U," was the first song since the group debuted to place at the top of the music charts.

Bang! Tan!

Bang! Tan!

The tickets for the concert held in Sidney, Australia were sold out in 5 minutes. Concerts held in the U.S., Mexico, Brazil, and Chile were also sold out, proving just how popular BTS had become.

On November 30th, 2015, "Run," the title song for their fourth mini-album *The Most Beautiful Moment in Life Pt. 2*, not only topped Korean music charts, but also placed 171st in the Billboard Top 200 Chart. This was the first time BTS was listed in the U.S. charts.

BTS performed tirelessly, continuing their 'The Most Beautiful Moment in Life ON STAGE' concert without rest.

A few days later, SUGA, who felt guilty about the concert being cancelled, revisited the World Memorial Hall in Kobe.

Videos and pictures of BTS were shared all over social media, including Twitter, YouTube, Facebook, and VLive. BTS worked harder to show their fans the same love they were given.

- **Jimin and V's dialogue** The two guys talked with Gyeongsang-do dialect. They are from Gyeongsang-do, South Korea.
- **Mandaggo** Gyeongsang-do dialect. It means 'Why would you do that?'.
- **Hwagae Market** It is located on the border of Gyeongsang-do and Jeolla-do. J-Hope, who is from Jeolla-do and SUGA, who is from Gyeongsang-do, compared themselves to Hwagae Market.

After winning several music awards at the end of 2015, BTS released a special album *The Most Beautiful Moment in Life: Young Forever* on May 2nd, 2016.

The album placed 107th on the Billboard 200 Chart. Songs in the album were also featured on the World Digital Song Chart.

On May 7th of the same year, BTS kicked off their fourth concert at the Olympic Gymnastics Arena in Seoul, followed by concerts in 10 cities in 7 Asian countries.

CHAPTER ★ 7

LOVE YOURSELF

Man, these concerts are tough. But it's great being so close to our fans.

That's why we can't slack off when it comes to our music.

Our fans are counting on us. Let's get to work on our next album.

Sounds good! And how about we each have our own solo track this time?

If we did that, we could show everyone our unique styles.

HMM...

What kind of lyrics would go well with this beat?

The Next Day

When we were trainees, I never imagined so many people would listen to our songs.

We have to work extra hard to repay their love. So let's get busy.

On February 13th, 2017, BTS released their special album *YOU NEVER WALK ALONE*.

Their title song "Spring Day" ranked 8th on the US iTunes song charts, making them the first K-POP group to make it into the top 10.

After promoting their second Korean studio album, *Wings*, BTS went on their second world-wide concert tour, '2017 BTS LIVE TRILOGY: EPISODE III. THE WINGS TOUR.'

BTS's influence and popularity snowballed with their performances at home and abroad.

• RM said that in Korean for Korean fans.

LOVE YOURSELF 'Her', the fifth mini-album was released on September 18th, 2017.

This album sold 1.37 million copies in Korea alone and also made it to the Korean music charts and many other global music charts including Billboard, showing the global popularity of BTS.

WHA!

BUZZ...

On November 1st, 2017, BTS launched a campaign with UNICEF, an international relief organization.

I think it's a good opportunity to return the love we have received in a way that goes beyond music.

I hope this campaign can console friends who did not have any social protection and give them the strength to carry on.

On November 27th, 2017, BTS was invited to *The Ellen Degeneres Show.*

I think teenagers in the States have come to relate to the words in BTS's songs.

Although the languages and cultures are different, we are happy that people everywhere can relate to our music.

BTS performed their first ever "MIC DROP" on TV. This song reached 28th in the Billboard top 100 chart, which was the highest ranking that any K-POP group has ever achieved. The next February, their album was certified gold from the Recording Industry Association of America. From there, they went on to appear on other programs in the States and showed the world that they are truly global superstars.

We are really going to appear on TV and go to the American Billboard Music Awards?

I think we've been really busy, huh?

That's why we always have to have gratitude in our hearts.

It's all thanks to our ARMY that we can have this warm welcome wherever we go in the world.

From December 8th to December 11th, 2017, the final concert of the 'WINGS TOUR' was held.

wow!

Bangtan!

Bangtan!

GOCHEOK
SKY DOME
고척스카이돔

ARMY everyone!

Some of you have said, "I am happy you have succeeded but I feel desolate because you are moving ahead and it seems I'm still stuck in a rut."

But, at first we didn't believe in ourselves, either. We were all scruffy and unprepared,

and didn't really know what we were doing. We didn't think we would succeed.

But you guys saw through all of that.

우리 함께라면, 사막도 바다가 돼

우리 함께라면, 사막도 바다가 돼

우리 함께라면, 사막도 바다가 돼

우리 함께라면, 사막도 바다가 돼

우리 함께라면, 사막도 바다가 돼

If we can give a little strength to your life and your dreams,

and we could lessen even some of the pains that you're going through, then we can feel worthy of your love.

It is certain that we are also going to have a lot of hardships in the future, but we know that all of you are supporting us.

That's why even when we hurt, we don't hurt. Even when we're sad, we're not sad, and even when we're afraid, we're not afraid because of all of you.

On May 18th, 2018, BTS's third regular album *LOVE YOURSELF 'Tear'* was released. This was the second album of the *LOVE YOURSELF* series.

This became #1 on the Billboard top 200 chart, and was ranked 10th in the Billboard Hot 100 chart, which was the first time a K-POP group placed in the top ten.

On May 22nd, 2018, BTS appears for the second consecutive year at the Billboard Music Awards.

BTS does not stop here. They continue with their active performance schedule in Korea. On August 24th, 2018, their third special album *LOVE YOURSELF 'Answer'* was released. This is the last album of the *LOVE YOURSELF* series. This also topped the Billboard 200 charts, reaching #1.

Since 2017, BTS has been working with UNICEF on a campaign. On September 24th of 2018, they gave a speech at the UN summit in New York.

On October 25th of that same year, they received a Hwagan medal at the Korea Popular Culture and Arts Award for their effort to promote Korean pop culture to the world. They were the youngest ever to receive the medal.

On February 10th, 2019, BTS became the first Korean idol group to attend the Grammy Awards.

While growing up in Korea, I always dreamed of being on the Grammy stage.

I thank all the people who have made our dreams come true. We will see you next year.

BTS became the first Korean group ever to be nominated for three major American music awards.

BTS held a 'LOVE YOURSELF' concert in Seoul at the Jamsil Stadium for two days on August 25th and 26th. They have created yet another new world view.

Our stage is getting bigger and bigger! I can't believe we are standing here at the Jamsil Stadium!

We promise to work harder and to give you a better performance every time!

To all the ARMY fans out there! I give you my love!

Starting in Seoul, BTS went on their world tour delivering messages of love and appreciation to their fans.

On April 12th, 2019, BTS released their sixth mini-album, *Map of the Seoul: Persona*, which is a follow-up to their *LOVE YOURSELF* series. The lead single, "Boy with Luv," a collaboration with Halsey, created a huge sensation with fans all over the world.

This album focuses on how we always try to hide ourselves around others. This is a message of trying to find your true self.

I PURPLE U!

BTS!

With their new album, *SPEAK YOURSELF*, BTS's world tour began. In June, 2019, they went to London's Wembley Stadium, where The Beatles, Michael Jackson, and Madonna had also performed.

ARMY!

BTS was the first South Korean group to give a solo performance that was broadcast live all over the world.

Korea's top pop idol group, BTS, is affecting people all around the world.

BTS's music gives comfort to all the weary people in the world despite language barriers. Flying on the wings of their eternal companion, the ARMY, BTS will deliver messages of hope to every corner of the earth.

Did you enjoy the story of BTS?

If you want to learn more, check out the appendix!
The appendix includes a lot more information
about BTS's music, a fun quiz, and
a tour of BTS's favorite places around Korea.
You have more chances to get closer to BTS!

APPENDIX

- KNOWLEDGE PLUS ❶ ❷ ❸

- UN SPEECH BY BTS

- BTS TRIVIA

- BANGTAN TOUR IN KOREA

- BTS TIMELINE

HOW BTS SUCCEEDED

BTS is the most beloved global boy band. They are the first K-pop group to reach the top of the Billboard Chart. They also have a large influence on music, fashion, style, and social activities around the world. What are the biggest reasons that BTS was able to become one of the top music groups in the world?

MUSIC WITH A MESSAGE

BTS, a group of seven attractive boys, has been singing songs with their own unique message since their debut in 2013. Unlike other idol groups, BTS has released an album every season, showcasing music of various genres.

"N.O" is a song in the *School Trilogy* album that was released in the first two years after their debut. The song contains a message about the young generation's dreams and perspectives about education, with lyrics like:

Fans at BTS World Tour Concert © LG Electronics

"Dream is gone, no time to breathe / School, house and PC room are all we have / We live the same life / And have to become number one." The *2-Part Youth* BTS album released in 2015 contains lyrics about stories of people in their twenties. The group expressed how the generation has to give up so many things ("Dope") and pointed out inequalities and underpaid jobs

BTS fans at K-Con 2017 in Mexico © Bonnielou2013

("Silver Spoon") through sophisticated melodies and impressive dance moves. With their perfect blend of social messages and performances, BTS underwent a new transition point when they released *The Most Beautiful Moment in Life* series. The group said they wanted to tell their stories and talk about "real things", and they did so by having all members write and compose their own songs that the younger generation can connect with.

In particular, the *LOVE YOURSELF* series albums that have been produced since March 2016 delivered a message that brought together fans around the world. BTS said that what they preach in the album "is not only about the personal experiences of a growing boy, but also about a message of reconciliation and harmony in the world." BTS said the album series was made to "begin loving myself," and while they haven't found the answers themselves, they hope that others will find them from the album series.

SELF-MAKING

The members of BTS were born and raised in Korea, where they all experienced the life of a typical Korean teenager. That is why they understand teenagers well and are able to infuse their own ideas and experiences into their albums. BTS trained to make their own music from the start so that they would be able to produce music that expresses sincere emotions. At first, critics had doubts about the lyrics and melodies, citing them to be a bit juvenile. However, BTS sensed that delivering their own stories would help them distinguish their own color and have a long career in the music industry. That is why they continued writing lyrics that directly expressed their innermost thoughts. Their sincerity and ability to empathize with the fans allowed BTS to move the hearts and minds of young people around the world. The songs in each of their albums come together and create one great story. Each and every song connects to generate a larger flow of ideas. Together, these stories unique to BTS are called the BTS Universe (BU).

BTS is loved by its global fandom "ARMY"
© Bonnielou2013

BTS songs have a positive impact on fans in many different ways. They provide an escape from a busy life and teach the fans how to love themselves.

SOCIAL MEDIA COMMUNICATION

BTS is famous for its communication with fans via social media platforms. The members show their free-spirited lives through video letters to fans and other off-the-record posts. Breaking away from the world of music idols, who are often shrouded in mystery, the members of BTS show their friendly faces to the fans, which often capture their hearts and minds. BTS began using social media to connect with fans prior to their debut. Through a channel called Bangtan Bomb, they have been sharing daily activities and work since June 19th, 2013. Even if fans are in faraway countries or have learned about

The popularity of BTS continues into the character industry. © Jeon Han

BTS long after their debut, they can watch videos on the YouTube Bangtan Bomb channel to understand the members' identities and characters. To this day, BTS continues to upload videos on many social media platforms. Even though they are constantly traveling around the world to perform music, BTS continues to post music and choreography videos on its official channel to communicate with fans worldwide. Fans who watch the videos create their own reaction videos or cover dance videos to further promote BTS to the rest of the world. Thanks to these efforts, YouTube produced an original film, *Burn the Stage*, which was released around the world.

BTS has a Twitter handle that opened on December 18th, 2012. Although Twitter is a social media platform for short 240-character messages, BTS posts YouTube links, article links, photos, and behind-the-scenes stories themselves, updating fans about their news on a real-time basis. Thanks to continuing uploads, the BTS Twitter handle became the first in Korea to have more than 10 million followers in November 2017. It also made the Guinness Book of World Records 2018 as the group most tweeted about in the world. Such communication with the fan base is the power behind BTS winning the Top Social Artist Award at the 2018 Billboard Music Awards.

방탄소년단 ✓
@BTS_twt

BTS always posts new stories on their social media channels. © BTS Twitter handle

GLOBAL MUSIC AWARDS

Award ceremonies are fun because we watch in anticipation of what awards our favorite music artists will win. In addition to Korean music award ceremonies, there are many such events around the world. Let's take a look at some of the music awards, such as the Billboard Music Awards, the Grammy's, and the American Music Awards.

THE BILLBOARD MUSIC AWARDS

The Billboard Music Awards are sponsored by Billboard, an American music magazine company. It was founded by William H. Donaldson and James Hennegan in Cincinnati on November 1ˢᵗ, 1894.

At first, *Billboard* published *Billboard Advertising*, which managed billboards placed near highways and streets. This magazine, which cost 10 cents per issue, worked to connect the advertisers and owners of billboards.

Several years later, *Billboard Advertising* began

Cover of *Billboard Advertising* in 1894
© Billboard Media Group

BTS's third regular album, which ranked first on the Billboard 200 Chart

to publish information about circuses, carnivals, amusement parks, whale shows, and other live performances. In 1909, *Billboard Advertising* began reporting on movies, featuring articles about topics people found interesting at the time. *Billboard* first began to write about music in 1913. It published a "sheet music best sellers and top songs in vaudeville theaters chart," which was not common. However, in the 1920s, it started to publish a chart of songs on the radio, and expanded the category with the development of the jukebox industry in the 1930s.

Because radio stations played music often, it was easier to organize music charts. In the beginning, there were three genres; pop, R&B, and country & western. In the 1950s, *Billboard* tapped into the TV entertainment industry by including program evaluation charts. The outdoor entertainment news, which had been a staple of the magazine, continued to be featured until the section was separated as a weekly magazine called *Amusement Business* in 1961.

In 1961, *Billboard* changed its name to *Billboard Music Week*. This is when the magazine started to discuss the music industry in its "Jukebox" section, along with jukeboxes and other entertainment devices.

A jukebox is a machine that plays music when coins are inserted. Pressing the button with the song of your choice would then play the music. The music that had the most plays would make the chart as the popular song of the week or the month. The magazine later simplified its name to *Billboard* and has since been covering the overall flow of the music industry. Today, it hosts the Billboard Music Awards to designate albums and musicians of the year. There are different categories, including artist of the year, male singer of the year, and female singer of the year, to measure the popularity of artists in almost all areas of popular music.

THE GRAMMY AWARDS

A Grammy Awards are the music award that has the most authority in the world. Originating in the United States on May 4th, 1959, the Grammy Awards are given for different genres, from pop to the classics, in 43 categories including best record, album, song, singer, production, and much more. Winners are determined by votes from the NARAS, who are musicians, music industry officials, producers, and studio engineers.

Grammy Awards trophy. Grammy is a nickname for gramophone. © Raga30

The members consider album sales, popularity on the charts, musical skills of the artist, artistic qualities, performance, innovative achievements in recording technology, and historical importance.

Adele, who won five Grammy Awards in 2017 © Marc E.

In addition to the main awards, the Grammy Awards also honor albums that have been around for more than 25 years with high artistic quality and historical significance. The lifetime award is made to recognize musicians who made outstanding artistic achievements. The Latin Grammy Awards were also established in 2000 to celebrate Latin music. The Grammy Awards are recognized for its authority because they determine winners based on a variety of factors, such as musical skills, artistic qualities, recording, and historical significance, but some criticize that it excludes non-English-speaking artists and their music. The most anticipated categories of the Grammy Awards are the record of the year, album of the year, song of the year, and rookie of the year. The awards are given not only to singers, but also to producers and engineers who participated in the production of the album.

THE AMERICAN MUSIC AWARDS

The American Music Awards have a special place in the hearts of Korean people, because it is the award show where Psy, who swept the world with his song "Gangnam Style," won a new media award and gave a finale performance with MC Hammer. In 2018, BTS was invited to the American Music Awards, where they won in the favorite social artist category and gave a highlight performance following the win. The American Music Awards was created by the American TV show host Dick Clark in 1973. Its history is shorter than that of the Billboard and the Grammys, but its influence is still significant. Unlike other award shows, the American Music Awards determine winners based on record and digital sales, broadcasting, and social media activity. The awards contain 29 categories. In addition to the artist of the year and rookie of the year awards, the favorite social artist award category was added in 2018. The ever increasing number of awards and presentations show the continued influence and reinvention of music throughout the world.

Taylor Swift, who won the artist of the year award at the American Music Awards in 2018 © GabboT

THE REASON
K-POP IS POPULAR

Before K-pop became widely popular, Korea was always the receiver of global music trends. Now that K-pop artists are popular overseas with a large fan base, people from all over the world visit Korea to attend concerts. Global fans love K-pop musicians, and even in the U.S., where pop music was born, there are many fans of K-pop. Let's take a look at how K-pop became so popular around the world!

ADDICTIVE SONGS

K-pop melodies are addictive and easy for anyone to follow. Since music by K-pop idols has to be memorable to stay in the charts for a long time, most K-pop songs are made to be addictive. Songs with repeated refrains are called "hook songs," and there is a reason that they were born in the context of K-pop.

K-Con Concert in the U.S. © Peter Kaminski

Korean pop music was created by localizing pop music from the West. When artists started to differentiate their songs to survive in the market, they created "hook songs" to provide fans with a unique sort of entertainment that is not found in pop music from the West. In addition, Korean artists collaborated with foreign composers to produce music that overseas fans could relate to with ease. Some may say that "hook songs" are less musically valuable, because they focus solely on popular appeal rather than artistic quality. This weakness is alleviated through the colorful performances of K-pop artists.

COLORFUL PERFORMANCES

Global fans appreciate K-pop artists that have choreography for each of their songs. They find it interesting that the musicians are able to sing and execute difficult movements at the same time.

There were dance groups, such as New Kids on the Block, NSync, and Backstreet Boys in the U.S. before, but many of these groups in the teen pop genre have disappeared. Years later, solo artists such as Ariana Grande and Selena Gomez led the teen pop market, but their focus lies more on their singing abilities rather than dance moves. Bruno Mars and Justin Bieber,

Spice Girls are a British girl group who has sold the most albums. One of the members is married to the soccer player David Beckham.
© Ezekiel

who are also famous in Korea, dance in their performances, but this is not considered a normal trend in the U.S. pop market.

In contrast, the Korean music industry, which was strongly influenced by Japanese idol groups and British and American pop music, train their artists in singing and dancing before their debit.

Fans dancing to BTS's music at K-Con © Bonnielon 2013

In the Western hemisphere, where dance music is all but gone, as well as Europe and South/Central America, where youth-driven pop culture was beginning to boom, K-pop became inevitably popular due to the artists' polished skills in both dancing and singing. K-pop groups typically have a lead dancer. The artists are led by the main dancer to showcase highly refined and uniform dance moves that attract the attention of the audience. These idols, who dance in unique and amazing choreography that blend into their songs, practice for months before they can perfectly execute the moves. This may be why choreography practice videos of K-pop groups get more than 10 million views when they are uploaded. And because more fans are posting videos of themselves singing and dancing like their favorite idols, K-pop is becoming more influential around the world.

GLOBALLY RECOGNIZED K-POP ARTISTS

K-pop artists are also recognized for the artistic quality of their albums and songs, and are certified by industry authorities. The U.S. Recording Industry Association of America (RIAA) certifies artists based on their digital single and regular album sales with designations such as Gold (500,000 or more), Platinum (1 million or more), Multi-Platinum (2 million or more), and Diamond (10 million or more). BTS's album *LOVE YOURSELF: Answer* received Gold certification from RIAA, making BTS the first Korean musician to receive recognition in the album category. Not only that, the title song for the album, "IDOL," also received Gold certification. In addition, other singles such as "DNA" and

BTS
Title: MIC DROP
Certification Date: February 6, 2018
Label: BIGHIT ENTERTAINMENT
Format: SINGLE

SHARE ⤴   MORE DETAILS ▼

Release Date. September 18, 2017
Category: None
Type: Digital
Certified Units: 0.5 Million
Genre: WORLD MUSIC
Previous Certification:
Gold | February 6, 2018

BTS's "Mic Drop," the first K-pop group's album to receive RIAA Gold Certification
© RIAA

"FAKE LOVE" also received Gold certification, and "MIC Drop (remix)" even received Platinum certification. With four songs and one album receiving RIAA certifications, BTS set a new record as a Korean artist group.

In 2012, Psy received Multi-Platinum certification from RIAA for his song "Gangnam Style." The fact that BTS and Psy received these certifications, having albums in non-English format, proves the elevated status of K-pop. BTS also received certifications in Japan, winning Gold (100,000 albums sold), Platinum (250,000), and Multi-Platinum (500,000) certifications. This demonstrates that BTS is a K-pop group that excites the world when they release an album. Acknowledging these achievements, the Korean government awarded the Hwagwan Order of Cultural Merit, given to people who contributed to cultural development, to BTS on October 24th, 2018. The group was the youngest to receive this honor.

The group TWICE also became a K-pop girl group recognized around the world. *BDZ*, their first regular album released in Japan, placed at the top of the Oricon Weekly Single and Album Charts. This is the first time in 6 years that foreign female artists have made such an achievement. In addition to this album, TWICE also received Platinum certification for all of their regular and single albums that were released in Japan.

Gold and Platinum albums certified by the U.S. Recording Industry Association of America (RIAA)
© Deidre Woodlard

The Full UN Speech by RM of BTS

My name is Kim Nam-joon, also known as RM, the leader of the group BTS. It is an incredible honor to be invited to an occasion with such significance for today's young generation.

Last November, BTS launched the 'LOVE MYSELF' campaign with UNICEF built on our belief that "true love first begins with loving myself." We've been partnering with UNICEF's '#ENDviolence' program to protect children and young people all over the world from violence. And our fans have become a major part of this campaign with their action and with their enthusiasm. We truly have the best fans in the world.

I'd like to begin by talking about myself. I was born in Ilsan, a city near Seoul, South Korea. It is a really beautiful place with a lake, hills, and even an annual flower festival. I spent a very happy childhood there, and I was just an ordinary boy. I used to look up at the night sky and wonder, and I used to dream the dreams of a boy. I used to imagine that I was a super hero who could save the world. In an intro to one of our early albums, there's a line that says, "My heart stopped when I was maybe nine or ten."

Looking back, I think that's when I began to worry about what other people thought of me and started seeing myself through their eyes. I stopped looking up at the night skies, the stars. I stopped daydreaming. Instead, I just tried to jam myself into the molds that other people made. Soon, I began to shut out my own voice and started to listen to the voices of others. No one called out my name, and neither did I. My heart stopped, and my eyes closed shut.

So, like this, I, we, all lost our names. We became like ghosts. But I had one sanctuary, and that was music.

There was a small voice inside of me that said, "Wake up, man, and listen to yourself." But it took me quite a long time to hear music calling my real name. Even after making the decision to join BTS, there were a lot of hurdles. Some people may not believe, but most people thought we were hopeless. Sometimes I just wanted to quit. But I think I was very lucky that I didn't give it all up. And I'm sure that I, and we, will keep stumbling and falling like this.

BTS has become artists performing in those huge stadiums and selling millions of albums right now, but I am still an ordinary 24-year-old guy. If there's anything that I've achieved, it was only possible that I have my other BTS members right by my side, and because of the love and support that our ARMY fans all over the world make for us.

And maybe I made a mistake yesterday, but yesterday's me is still me. Today, I am who I am with all of my faults and my mistakes. Tomorrow, I might be a tiny bit wiser, and that'll be me too. These faults and mistakes are what I am, making up the brightest stars in the constellation of my life. I have come to love myself for who I am, for who I was, and for who I hope to become.

I'd like to say the one last thing. After releasing our *LOVE YOURSELF* albums and launching the 'LOVE MYSELF' campaign, we started to hear remarkable stories from our fans all over the world. How our message helped them overcome their hardships in life and start loving themselves. Those stories constantly remind us of our responsibility.

So let's take all one more step. We have learned to love ourselves, so now I urge you to "Speak yourself." I'd like to ask all of you. What is your name? What excites you and makes your heart beat? Tell me your story. I want to hear your voice, and I want to hear your conviction. No matter who you are, where you're from, your skin color, your gender identity —just speak yourself. Find your name and find your voice by speaking yourself.

I'm Kim Nam-joon, and also RM of BTS. I am an idol, and I am an artist from a small town in Korea. Like most people, I've made many and plenty mistakes in my life. I have many faults, and I have many more fears, but I'm going to embrace myself as hard as I can, and I'm starting to love myself gradually, just little by little.

What is your name? Speak yourself.

Thank you very much.

Hello, fans!
Let's learn more about BTS

 When did BTS debut?

① June 12th, 2013   ② June 13th, 2013

③ June 14th, 2013   ④ June 15th, 2013

 Which song is not included in BTS's 2nd regular album *WINGS*?

① Intro: Boy Meets Evil   ② BTS Cypher 4

③ Am I Wrong   ④ Gangnam Style

 In which order did the members join BTS?

① RM – SUGA – J-Hope – Jungkook – V – Jimin – Jin

② RM – Jin – SUGA – Jungkook – J-Hope – V – Jimin

③ RM – SUGA – J-Hope – Jin – Jungkook – V – Jimin

④ RM – J-Hope – SUGA – Jungkook – V – Jimin – Jin

 Which is not a correct destination and year of the 'BTS Summer Package'?

① Wanju, Jeollabuk-do, 2019   ② Kota Kinabalu, 2015

③ Palawan, 2018   ④ Dubai, 2016

5 **Whose headgear was not taken off or didn't run down in the BTS Bomb video Appeal Ver.?**

① SUGA   ② Jimin   ③ Jungkook   ④ V

6 Which song does not have a rap line?

① BTS Cypher PT.3 : KILLER   ② Tear

③ 전하지 못한 진심 (The Truth Untold)   ④ BTS Cypher PT.2 : Triptych

7 What is not a correct pairing of the role and member from "21st Century Girl" Halloween Ver.?

① Jimin – Chinese cabbage   ② Jungkook – Rabbit

③ Jin – Cowboy   ④ J-Hope – Scholar

8 Who hasn't worked in collaboration with BTS?

① Seong-jin Cho   ② So-ra Lee   ③ Halsey   ④ Wale

9 Which stage name and birthday pair is incorrect?

① J-Hope – February 18th, 1994

② SUGA – March 8th, 1993

③ V – December 30th, 1995

④ Jin – December 4th, 1992

10 BTS was placed on the Billboard Hot 100 chart with "Fake Love" on May 29th, 2018. What was the first entry ranking in the chart?

① 8th ② 10th ③ 23rd ④ 101st

OMG!

Answers : 1② 2② 3① 4③ 5④ 6③ 7④ 8① 9② 10②

RM Forest

Location: In front of the clock tower at Jamsil Han River Park

RM Forest was created to celebrate RM's 26th birthday. The Korean Federation for Environmental Movement and the fans gathered to build a forest named RM Forest. They built a forest of 1,200 spiraea prunifolia (also known as bridal wreath) trees in a show of support for the musician's known commitment to environmental protection to reduce fine dust and respond to climate change.

Besides, the good deeds of the BTS lead the participation of the fans who share their values, showing a 'good influence' to various parts of society by participating in donations.

Iryeong Station Platform

Location: Samsang-ri, Jangheung-myeon, Yangju-si, Gyeonggi-do

This is the place for the music video for "Spring Day," the title song of the special album *YOU NEVER WALK ALONE*. Iryeong Station is where you can see V waiting for a train at a snowy station. Since the music video was released, there are more foreign tourists taking winter trips in Korea. The train station is in a suburb of Seoul, located between Byuckje station and Jangheung station. Since the end of the operation of passenger trains in 2004, only freight trains operate.

Jumunjin Hyangho Beach Bus Stop

Location: Jumunjin, Gangneung-si, Gangwon-do

This is Jumunjin Hyangho Beach BTS bus stop, which is where BTS's *YOU NEVER WALK ALONE* album jacket was filmed. It wasn't taken from an existing bus stop, but it was built for the BTS album jacket. After the shooting, the bus stop was removed. But Gangneung-si reproduced the bus stop for tourists.

Can you realize how popular BTS is to reproduce the shooting sets because of ARMY?

Hyangiram Temple

Location: Dolsan-eup, Yeosu-si, Jeollanam-do

The leader of BTS, RM visited here and became famous among the ARMY. BTS's public pictures on Twitter included a picture of RM following a humorous expression sitting next to Cheonjin Buddha. Because of how cute RM is, ARMY also visits Hyangiram and takes pilgrimages while taking pictures with the same pose. Hyangiram is also famous as a sunrise spot in the South Sea.

© YonhapNews

© YonhapNews

Line Friends Flagship Store

Location 1: Itaewon-ro, Yongsan-gu, Seoul
Location 2: Yanghwa-ro, Mapo-gu, Seoul

This is a character shop of BT21. BT21 is a character born through the collaboration between BTS and Line Friends. The character of BT21 participated in the entire process of the character's birth with members of the BTS sketching the characters and embodying their characteristics.

RM's KOYA, Jin's RJ, SUGA's SHOOKY, J-Hope's MANG, Jimin's CHIMMY, V's TATA, Jungkook's COOKY and ARMY's VAN. There are eight total characters. There is a storyline that TATA, the prince of BT Planet, meets six members and creates BT21, a dream of the best star in the universe. BT21 is very popular with the ARMY members through launching various character products.

Damyang Metasequoia Road

Location: Hakdong-ri, Damyang-eup, Damyang-gun, Jeollanam-do

On March, 2019, the leader of BTS, RM, posted on Twitter, "a lot of our ARMY is visiting Metasequoia Road." The Metasequoia Road in Damyang is the largest in Korea, and was named a 'Beautiful Street Forest' by the Korea Forest Service in 2002. It is expected that more tourists will visit from all over the country to follow in the footsteps of RM.

© YonhapNews

Gyeongchun Line Forest Road

Location 1: Gyeongchun railway bridge (Wolgye-dong, Nowon-gu) ~ Damter Village (Gongneung-dong, Nowon-gu) about 6 km
Location 2: Line 6 Hwarangdae station exit 2, Line 1 Wolgye station exit 4, Gyeongchun line Galmae station exit 2

Gyeongchun Line Forest Road is where Gyeongchun Line, which has been neglected since the train operation was stopped, began to be constructed as a forest road in Seoul in 2013. In May 2019, the construction of the entire section spanning 6 km from stage 1 to stage 3 was completed. The third stage, which was opened last, is popular as a place where you can enjoy a trip through the past with nature.

If you visit Gyeongchun Line Forest Road, around the Hwarangdae station, you can also find the place where RM took a picture. RM's footprint is there where he stopped so that tourists could feel the presence of BTS.

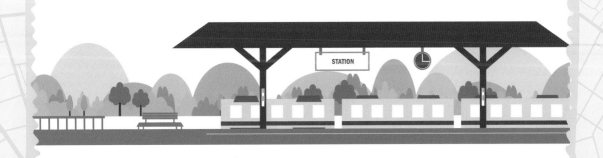

June 12th, 2013	Release, debut showcase of Single Album *2 COOL 4 SKOOL*
June 13th, 2013	Debut
September 11th, 2013	Release of Mini-Album Vol. 1 *O!RUL8,2?*
November 14th, 2013	First Rookie Award at Melon Music Awards
February 12th, 2014	Release of Mini-Album Vol. 2 *Skool Luv Affair*
March 29th, 2014	First fan meeting, the opening ceremony of the fan club '2014 BTS: 1st Fan Meeting MUSTER'
May 14th, 2014	Release of Special Album *SKOOL LUV AFFAIR SPECIAL ADDITION*
June 4th, 2014	Debut in Japan with Japanese Single Album *No More Dream (Japanese Ver.)*
August 20th, 2014	Release of the First Album *DARK & WILD*
October 17th, 2014	First solo concert 'BTS LIVE TRILOGY EPISODE II, THE RED BULLET'
March 28th, 2015	Concert 'BTS LIVE TRILOGY EPISODE I, BTS BEGINS'
April 29th, 2015	Release of Mini-Album Vol. 3 *The Most Beautiful Moment in Life Pt. 1*
May 5th, 2015	SBS MTV *The Show* "I NEED U" the first place in music broadcasting
May 8th, 2015	KBS *Music Bank* "I NEED U" the first place in terrestrial broadcasting
November 27th, 2015	Concert 'BTS LIVE The Most Beautiful Moment in Life ON STAGE'
November 30th, 2015	Release of Mini-Album Vol. 4 *The Most Beautiful Moment in Life Pt. 2*
December 7th, 2015	Billboard 200 Chart first entry
January 24th, 2016	Fan Meeting, 'BTS 2nd MUSTER [ZIP CODE: 22920]'
May 2nd, 2016	Release of Special Album *The Most Beautiful Moment in Life: Young Forever*
May 7th, 2016	Concert 'BTS LIVE The Most Beautiful Moment in Life ON STAGE: EPILOGUE' first concert in Gymnastics Stadium
October 10th, 2016	Release of Regular Album Vol. 2 *WINGS*
November 12th, 2016	Fan Meeting, 'BTS 3rd MUSTER [ARMY.ZIP+]'
November 19th, 2016	First Grand Prize at Melon Music Awards
February 13th, 2017	Release of Special Album *YOU NEVER WALK ALONE*
February 18th, 2017	Concert 'BTS LIVE TRILOGY EPISODE III, THE WINGS TOUR'

May 21st, 2017	Billboard Music Awards 'Top Social Artist' first prize
August 16th, 2017	Release "LOVE YOURSELF Highlight Reel 起"
September 18th, 2017	Release of Mini-Album Vol. 5 *LOVE YOURSELF 承 'HER'*
September 26th, 2017	Billboard Hot 100 Chart First Entry
November 19th, 2017	American Music Awards Performance, US terrestrial TV broadcast debut
December 8th, 2017	Concert 'BTS LIVE TRILOGY EPISODE III, THE WINGS TOUR THE FINAL'
January 13th, 2018	Fan Meeting, 'BTS 4th MUSTER [Happy Ever After]'
May 18th, 2018	Release of Regular Album Vol. 3 *LOVE YOURSELF 轉 'Tear'*
August 24th, 2018	Release of Regular Album Vol. 3 Special *LOVE YOURSELF 結 'Answer'*
August 25th, 2018	Concert 'BTS WORLD TOUR LOVE YOURSELF', first concert in Jamsil Sports Complex Olympic Main Stadium
September 24th, 2018	Speech 'UNICEF Youth Agenda Generation Unlimited Event', New York UN Headquarters
November 6th, 2018	First Popularity Award at Genie Music Awards
November 15th, 2018	Movie release *Burn the Stage: The Movie*
January 26th, 2019	Movie release *LOVE YOURSELF in Seoul*
February 10th, 2019	Presented an award, Grammy Award for Best R&B Album Category
April 12th, 2019	Release of Mini-Album Vol. 6 *MAP OF THE SOUL: PERSONA*
May 1st, 2019	Billboard Music Awards, First Prize 'Top Duo/Group'
May 4th, 2019	World Stadium Tour, a first for korean singers 'BTS WORLD TOUR LOVE YOURSELF: SPEAK YOURSELF'
August 7th, 2019	Movie release *Bring the Soul: The Movie*
October 26th, 2019	Concert 'BTS WORLD TOUR LOVE YOURSELF: SPEAK YOURSELF [THE FINAL]'
November 24th, 2019	American Music Awards: 'Favorite Duo or Group Award (Pop/Rock)', 'Tour of the Year Award', 'Favorite Social Artist Award'

"You are more beautiful than Seoul.
We will love you more than yesterday,
less than tomorrow."